Garfield

Another Serve

BY: JIM DAVIS

RAVETTE BOOKS

This edition first published by
Ravette Books Limited 1987

Reprinted 1988, 1989

Printed in Great Britain
for Ravette Books Limited,
3 Glenside Estate, Star Road, Partridge Green,
Horsham, West Sussex RH13 8RA
by The Guernsey Press Company Limited,
Guernsey, Channel Islands
and bound by
WBC Bookbinders Limited,
Maesteg, Mid Glamorgan.

ISBN 0 948456 55 8

Another Serve

Garfield stirs up a heapful of laughs with his special recipe of home style humour and wit. Readers will digest the gastronomical exploits of our 'culinary cat' as he makes a meal of everyday situations. The results, even for Garfield, are sometimes a bit hard to swallow.

2-4

AREN'T PET STORES FASCINATING, GARFIELD?

THE CUTE HAMSTERS, THE CANARIES, THE TROPICAL FISH

4-12

GARFIELD?

GARFIELD?!!

OH, THERE YOU ARE

COME ON. LET'S GO HOME FOR LUNCH

NO THANKS. I JUST ATE

JIM DAVIS

I'M BORED

6·21

BORED, BORED, BORED

THERE MUST BE MORE THINGS TO DO ON A SCREEN DOOR THAN JUST HANG HERE

JIM DAVIS

NICE GOING, DUMMY

GARFIELD. LASAGNA!

JIM DAVIS

I WAXED THE TABLE TODAY

WHEN MY BONES KNIT, YOU ARE A DEAD MAN

8-2

PAT
PAT
PAT

JiM DAViS

POOMP!

I WOULD HAVE
HAD TO EAT HIM
TO SAVE FACE

8-16

HEY, GARFIELD, GUESS WHAT?

THE DOG NEXT DOOR IS BEING GIVEN A BIRTHDAY PARTY TODAY

THIS BRICK SHOULD MAKE A SPIFFY GIFT

BONK YIP!

YIP!

'APPY BIRTHDAY, DOG

HELLO, DOCTOR? DO YOU THINK YOU COULD SURGICALLY REMOVE MY CAT FROM A DOG

8-23

JIM DAVIS

GOOD MORNING, GARFIELD

© 1981 United Feature Syndicate, Inc.

SLUP

8-30

GOOD MORNING

JIM DAVIS

I'LL HAVE A STEAK, FRIES AND A LARGE COLA

AND MY CAT HERE WILL HAVE AN ORDER OF LASAGNA

WHAP!

MAKE THAT A DOUBLE ORDER

© 1981 United Feature Syndicate, Inc.

BONK!

PERHAPS A TRIPLE ORDER

GOOSH!

HECK WITH IT. GIVE HIM THE WHOLE PAN

AND GIVE IT WINGS

9-6 JIM DAVIS

Jim Davis 9-13

© 1981 United Feature Syndicate, Inc.

RATS!

I WENT AND DID IT AGAIN

HERE I AM, DOOMED TO DIE AGAIN. IF I STAY UP HERE I'LL STARVE. IF I JUMP I'LL BECOME A CAT PANCAKE. I HOPE SOMEONE RESCUES ME

STUCK UP THE TREE AGAIN, GARFIELD?

HELP! HELP!

DIAL
DIAL
DIAL

HELLO, JOE'S GARAGE? CAN YOU LOOK AT MY CAR?

I'D LIKE TO BRING HIM IN FOR A CHECKUP

BUT I JUST HAD ONE

YOU'D BETTER FLUSH OUT HIS SYSTEM...

TIGHTEN HIS HOSES

© 1981 United Feature Syndicate, Inc.

REPLACE ALL THE WORN PARTS

OH YES, AND HAVE HIM REUPHOLSTERED

GARFIELD?

ABU DHABI

JIM DAVIS   10-4

YOU KNOW, SOME FOODS ARE FUNNIER THAN OTHERS

10-18   JIM DAVIS

BEETS ARE FUNNY

LIVER... NOT FUNNY

PRUNES ARE FUNNY, POTATOES AREN'T

CHICKEN, NOW THAT'S FUNNY

© 1981 United Feature Syndicate, Inc.

HOW ABOUT PICKLES AND KUMQUATS FOR LUNCH, GARFIELD?

WAH HA HA!

11-22

JIM DAVIS

TIME PASSES SLOWLY ON A WEEKEND

A FLY CRAWLS UP THE WALL

ONE OF THOSE IRIDESCENT FLYS OF FALL

TIME PASSES SLOWLY ON A WEEKEND

THAT'S MY JON. HE'S RAISED BOREDOM TO AN ART FORM

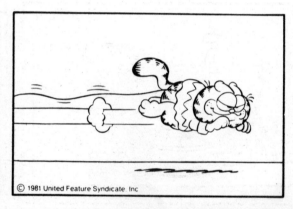

GARFIELD

© 1985 United Feature Syndicate, Inc.

JIM DAVIS 1-27

GARFIELD

SIGH

GARFIELD, YOU ARE WORTHLESS. DO YOU KNOW THAT?

YOU ARE DOING ZERO WITH YOUR LIFE,.... ZIP. DO YOU KNOW THAT?

POKE POKE

© 1985 United Feature Syndicate, Inc.

YOU SHOULD LEARN SOMETHING NEW EACH DAY. IT WOULD LEND PURPOSE TO THIS DREARY EXISTENCE OF YOURS

I'M GOING TO THE STORE. WHEN I COME BACK, I WANT YOU TO HAVE LEARNED SOMETHING

JIM DAVIS   3-10

TIME PASSES

I'M HOME, GARFIELD. DID YOU LEARN ANYTHING?

I LEARNED HOW TO USE YOUR CREDIT CARD

GARFIELD

WE'LL BE RIGHT BACK AFTER THIS WORD FROM OUR SPONSOR

QUICK, GARFIELD! DURING THE COMMERCIAL LET'S GET SOME POPCORN!

© 1985 United Feature Syndicate, Inc.

I'LL TAKE CARE OF THE BUTTER, BOWLS AND NAPKINS. YOU TAKE CARE OF THE POPCORN!

I GOT MY STUFF. ARE YOU TAKING CARE OF THE POPCORN?!

YUP!

SLAM

WELCOME BACK

WE MADE IT!

JIM DAVIS 4-7

WHERE'S THE POPCORN?

(BURP) I TOOK CARE OF IT

GARFIELD

COME HERE, GARFIELD. I HAVE SOMETHING TO TELL YOU

I'M GOING TO ORGANIZE MY SOCK DRAWER TODAY

THIS IS A RED-LETTER DAY!

I'M GOING TO PUT THE BLACK ONES ON ONE END AND THE WHITE ONES ON THE OTHER

DECISIONS! DECISIONS! DECISIONS!

AND DO YOU KNOW WHAT I MIGHT DO AFTER THAT?

OH NO! SPARE ME! SPARE ME!

I MIGHT TIGHTEN THE HINGES ON MY READING GLASSES

ARRRGH!

JIM DAVIS 5-19

© 1985 United Feature Syndicate, Inc.

OH WHEN WILL THIS MAD, CRAZY, MERRY-GO-ROUND EXISTENCE EVER END?

OR I MIGHT GIVE A CERTAIN WISE GUY CAT A BATH

I'LL TUCK, YOU SORT

PERSONS AT WORK

HOW FORTUITOUS, SOMEONE WAS KIND ENOUGH TO DIG THIS HOLE FOR ME

© 1985 United Feature Syndicate Inc

I'LL COVER IT WITH THESE BRANCHES AND PLAY A LITTLE TRICK ON ODIE

HEY, ODIE, HAVE A BONE

BOING!

SOMETHING'S NOT RIGHT HERE

OH NO! IT'S THE OLD RUBBER HOLE GAG!

JIM DAVIS 6-16

GARFIELD

LET'S SEE, IT'S OVER AND UNDER, THEN THROUGH

I'M TAKING YOU OUT TO EAT, GARFIELD. YOU'LL HAVE TO WEAR THIS TO GET INTO THE RESTAURANT

© 1985 United Feature Syndicate, Inc.

I'LL HAVE A STEAK AND MY CA...ER...SON HERE WILL HAVE A TRIPLE ORDER OF LASAGNA AND A CUP OF COCOA

THIS IS AN EXCLUSIVE RESTAURANT, GARFIELD. USE YOUR SILVERWARE

GULP! SLURP! GULP!

JIM DAVIS

THAT MARSHMALLOW IS MEANT FOR YOUR COCOA

7-7

HEH, HEH. DON'T LICK YOUR PAWS AT THE TABLE, SON

THAT'S THE RUDEST LITTLE KID I'VE EVER SEEN!

HE EVEN SHED ON THE TABLECLOTH

GARFIELD

KING CATTAEATALOTTA GIVES A PEACE OFFERING TO THE VOLCANO THAT CLAIMED YOUNG PRINCESS ANGORA

UP AGAINST THE WALL, YOU CRUMBUMS, OR I'LL GIVE YOUR BACKSIDES A TASTE OF MY DAISY!

MAKE LOVE, NOT DOG POUNDS

JIM DAVIS

7-14

HERE, MY DEAR. PERHAPS THIS WILL MAKE UP FOR LEAVING YOU ALONE TO FEND OFF THE BORDER GUARDS

AHEE AH-EE AH!

WHAT HAPPENED TO MY FLOWER BED?!

SCUTTLEBUTT AT THE PRECINCT IS THAT YOUR DAISIES WERE VANDALIZED BY AN OVERACTIVE IMAGINATION

GARFIELD

PET SHOP

LOOK AT ALL THOSE POOR ANIMALS IN THERE ALL CAGED UP. THIS LOOKS LIKE A JOB FOR...

FREEDOM FIGHTER!

YOU'RE FREE! YOU'RE FREE!

JIM DAVIS 9-8

GO FOR IT!

© 1985 United Feature Syndicate, Inc.

HMMM, FOLKS MUST NOT BE HEAVILY INTO FREEDOM THESE DAYS

YOU'RE SECURE! YOU'RE SECURE!

SLAM!

GARFIELD

ZIP

KISS

JIM DAVIS 9/22
© 1985 United Feature Syndicate, Inc.

A selection of Garfield books published by Ravette

Garfield Landscapes

Garfield The All-Round Sports Star	£2.95
Garfield The Irresistible	£2.95
Garfield On Vacation	£2.95
Garfield Weighs In	£2.95
Garfield I Hate Monday	£2.95
Garfield Special Delivery	£2.95
Garfield The Incurable Romantic	£2.95
Garfield Wraps It Up	£2.95
Garfield This Is Your Life	£2.95
Garfield Sheer Genius	£2.95
Garfield Goes Wild	£2.95

Garfield Pocket-books

No. 1 Garfield The Great Lover	£1.95
No. 2 Garfield Why Do You Hate Mondays?	£1.95
No. 3 Garfield Does Pooky Need You?	£1.95
No. 4 Garfield Admit It, Odie's OK!	£1.95
No. 5 Garfield Two's Company	£1.95
No. 6 Garfield What's Cooking?	£1.95
No. 7 Garfield Who's Talking?	£1.95
No. 8 Garfield Strikes Again	£1.95
No. 9 Garfield Here's Looking At You	£1.95
No. 10 Garfield We Love You Too	£1.95
No. 11 Garfield Here We Go Again	£1.95
No. 12 Garfield Life and Lasagne	£1.95
No. 13 Garfield In The Pink	£1.95
No. 14 Garfield Just Good Friends	£1.95
No. 15 Garfield Plays It Again	£1.95
No. 16 Garfield Flying High	£1.95
No. 17 Garfield On Top Of The World	£1.95
No. 18 Garfield Happy Landings	£1.95

Garfield TV Specials

Here Comes Garfield	£2.95
Garfield On The Town	£2.95
Garfield In The Rough	£2.95
Garfield In Disguise	£2.95
Garfield In Paradise	£2.95
Garfield Goes To Hollywood	£2.95
A Garfield Christmas	£2.95
The Second Garfield Treasury	£5.95
The Third Garfield Treasury	£5.95
The Fourth Garfield Treasury	£5.95
Garfield A Weekend Away	£4.95
Garfield How to Party	£3.95

All these books are available at your local bookshop or newsagent, or can be ordered direct from the publisher. Just tick the titles you require and fill in the form below. Prices and availability subject to change without notice.

Ravette Books Limited, 3 Glenside Estate, Star Road, Partridge Green, Horsham, West Sussex RH13 8RA

Please send a cheque or postal order, and allow the following for postage and packing. UK: Pocket-books – 45p for up to two books and 15p for each additional book. Landscape Series and TV Specials – 45p for one book plus 15p for each additional book. Treasuries, How to Party and A Weekend Away – 75p for each book.

Name..

Address...

....

[Handwritten note top right: "24 books 20 more books to collect"]